B m L S
a w x G
r Q P o e
u N T K
j z Y F
I V h D
c Z

Minnesota TWINS

FROM A TO Z

BARNES
& NOBLE
BOOKS

NEW YORK

**Created by the Minnesota Twins Wives Organization
for Twins fans of all ages.**

**Proceeds will benefit Upper Midwest charities and the Minnesota Twins Community Fund.
www.twinsbaseball.com**

O n behalf of the Minnesota Twins Wives Organization, Twins Community Fund, and the entire Minnesota Twins organization, thank you for purchasing **Minnesota Twins from A to Z.** We hope this book promotes reading in your family while celebrating all that is good about baseball and the Minnesota Twins.

We believe this book captures the essence and virtue of Twins Baseball, which is to provide quality, affordable family entertainment while striving to meet important community needs. Money raised from the sale of this book will benefit Upper Midwest charities and the Minnesota Twins Community Fund.

We appreciate your support of the Minnesota Twins and look forward to seeing you at a game or in the community.

Win Twins!

Corri Ford
Member, Twins Wives Organization
Board Member, Twins Community Fund

Dave St. Peter
President, Minnesota Twins
Board Member, Twins Community Fund

Aa

The Star-Spangled Banner

A is for the national **anthem** we all love to sing.

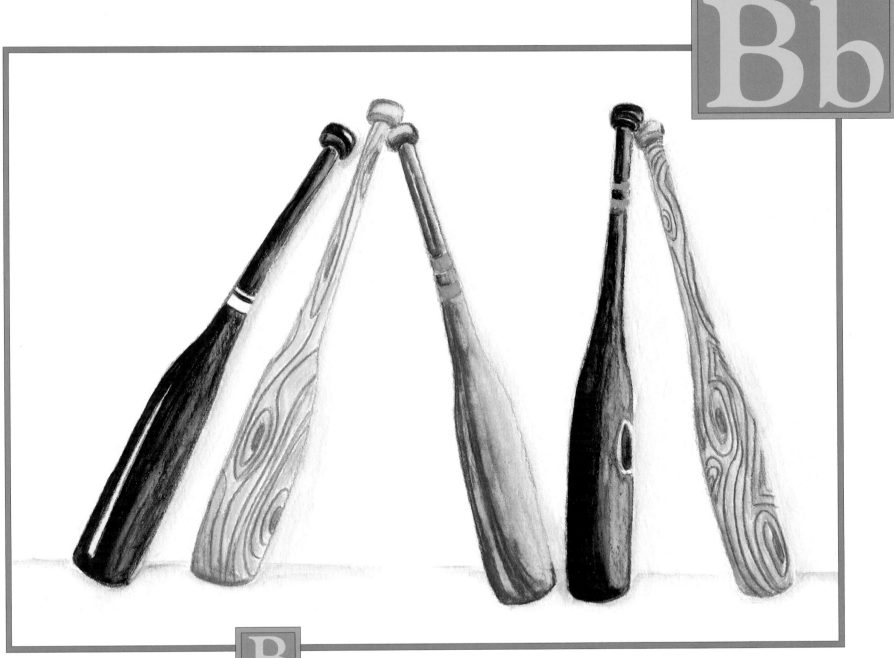

B is for **bats** that ballplayers swing.

Cc

C is for **cotton candy**, a treat that's fun.

D is for Dome Dogs wrapped in a bun.

E is for equipment like bats, balls, and tees.

F is for **fans** who wave their Homer Hankies!

G is for grand slam and a score that just grew.

H is for Hall of Famers Puckett and Carew.

Ii

I is for Twins helmets filled with ice cream.

J is for a **jumping** catch that makes the fans scream.

K is for Killebrew, a Twin of great fame.

L is for ballpark **lights** that shine each night game.

M is for the **Metrodome**, home of the Twins.

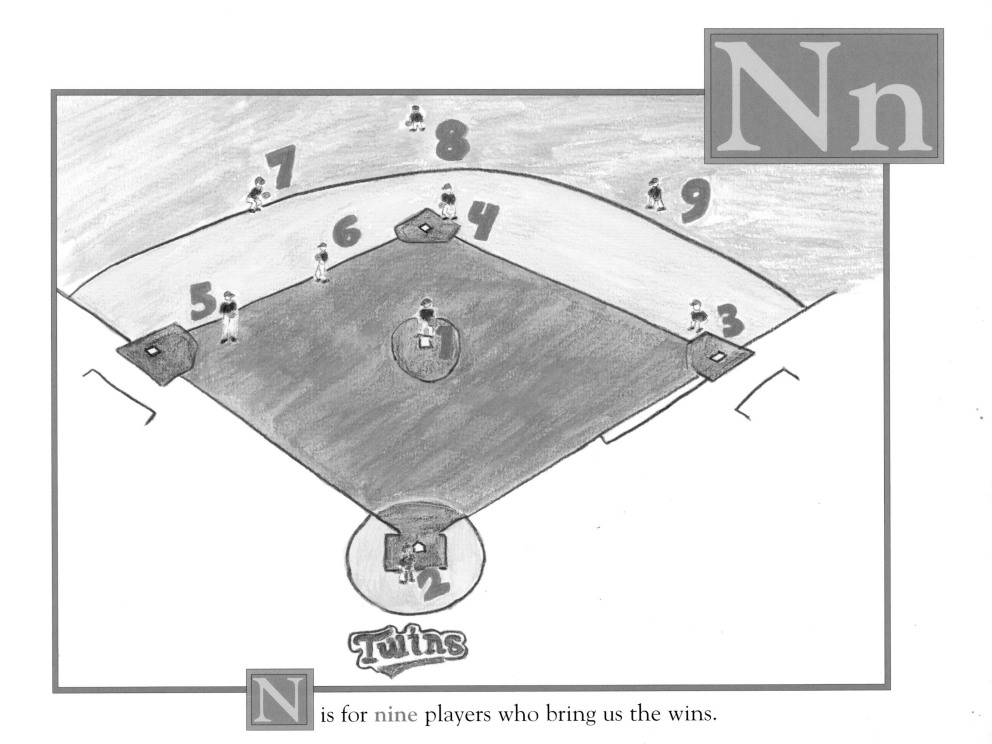

N is for nine players who bring us the wins.

O is for the **organ** with its great loud sound.

P is for the **pitcher** up on the mound.

Q is for the **quick** players out on the field.

Rr

R is for the **reliever** who refuses to yield.

S is for the **scoreboard** glowing at night.

T is for **T.C.**, who homers with might.

U is for the **umpire**, who calls "ball" or "strike."

♪ "Take me out to the ball game
Take me out with the crowd.
Buy me some peanuts
and Cracker Jacks. I don't care if I
ever get back. For it's root, root, root
for the home team, if they don't
win it's a shame. For it's one,
two, three strikes
you're out at the OLD BALL GAME!"

In memory of our Vendor
Roy Vavrosky

V is for the **vendor**, who sells treats we like.

W is for World Series champs in '87 and '91.

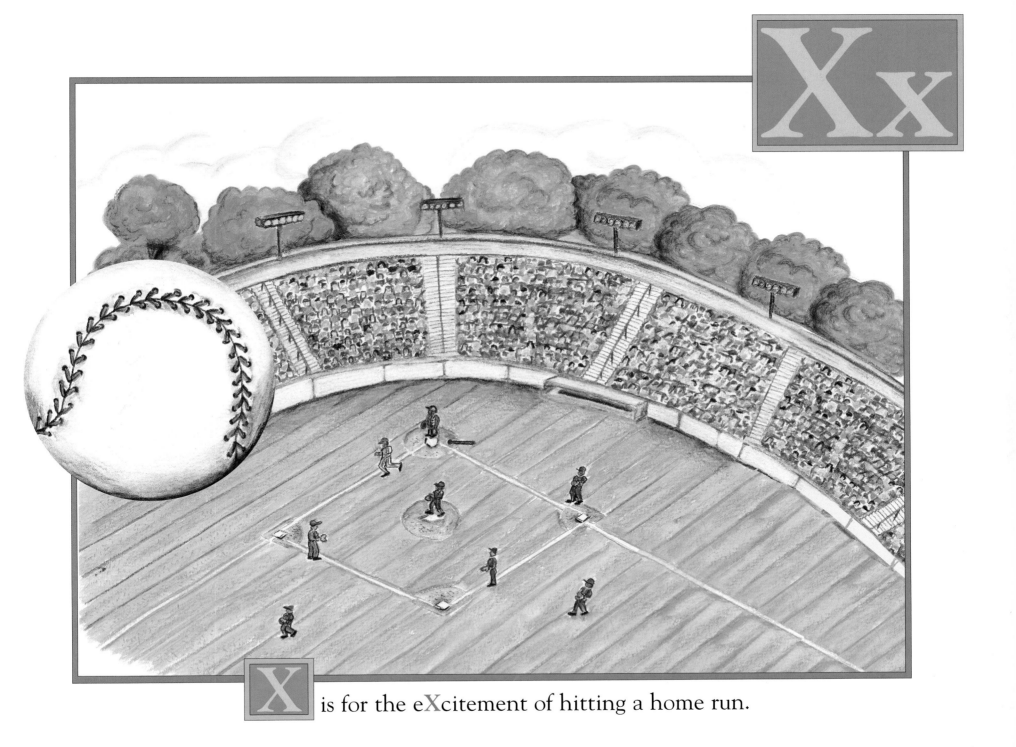

X is for the e**X**citement of hitting a home run.

Y is for screaming "Yeah!" when the Twins score!

Z is for a great day at the park–I hope I have more.

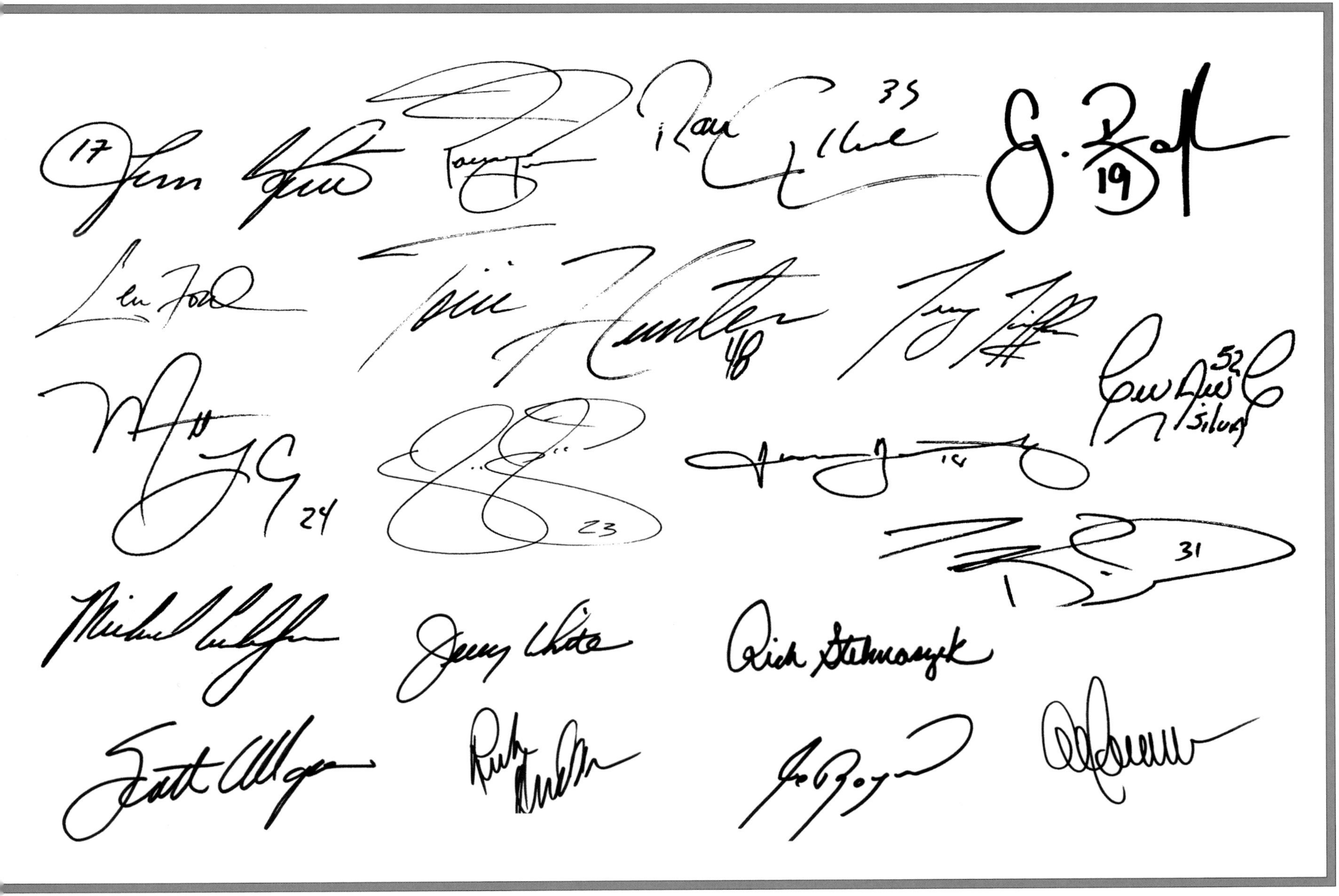

The Minnesota Twins
would like to thank those who made
Minnesota Twins from A to Z
a reality.

Twins Wives Organization
Becky Crain
Corri Ford
Katrina Hunter
Krista Jones
Holly LeCroy
Gabrielle Lohse
Mendi Mays
Lisa Nathan
Heather Radke
Michele Redmond
Erica Restovich
Roselen Rincon
Gina Rivas
Erin Romero
Yasmile Santana
Sharonda Stewart
Kelli Tiffee

Sketch Artist
Jodi Kerttu

Barnes & Noble
Barbara Morgan, Publisher
Leonard Vigliarolo, Graphic Designer

Minnesota Twins
Peter Martin

Printed in Canada

B m L s

a w x G

r Q P

u K o e

j N T

Y F

i V h D

c Z